GRIND

Dee Phillips

Evans

First published in 2009
by Evans Brothers Limited
2A Portman Mansions
Chiltern Street
London W1U 6NR
UK

Printed in Dubai

British Library Cataloguing in Publication Data
Phillips, Dee.
      Grind. -- (Right now)
      1. Graphic novels. 2. Young adult fiction.
      I. Title II. Series
      741.5-dc22
      ISBN-13: 9780237539573

Developed & Created by RUbY TUesdaY BooKS Ltd

Project Director – Ruth Owen
Head of Design – Elaine Wilkinson
Designer – Trudi Webb
Editor – Frances Ridley
Consultant – Lorraine Petersen, Chief Executive of NASEN
© Ruby Tuesday Books Limited 2009

ACKNOWLEDGEMENTS

With thanks to Lorraine Petersen, Chief Executive of NASEN for her help in the development and creation of these books.

Images courtesy of Shutterstock; **pages 1, 29, 30, 31, 32-33, 34-35** Andy Horsley; **pages 18-19 (main)** Superstock

While every effort has been made to secure permission to use copyright material, the publishers apologise for any errors or omissions in the above list and would be grateful for notification of any corrections to be included in subsequent editions.

I didn't want to move to this town.
There's nowhere to skate here.
I miss my friends.
I hate it here.

GRIND

ONE MOMENT CAN CHANGE YOUR LIFE FOREVER

My elbow hurts.
My knees hurt.
It's Saturday afternoon and
I'm lying outside the library.

My life
couldn't get any
worse!

5

I saw the handrail and I couldn't resist it.
I thought I could do it.
A nose grind down the handrail.

But I was wrong!

And now I'm lying outside the library. My new jeans are ripped.

My deck is stuck in a tree.

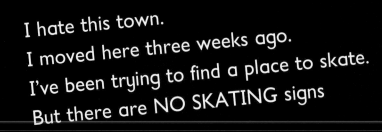

I hate this town.
I moved here three weeks ago.
I've been trying to find a place to skate.
But there are NO SKATING signs
everywhere.
If I get into trouble, Mum will go mad!

NO
SKATING
HERE

I moved here three weeks ago with Mum.
Mum is getting married to Paul.
I want Mum and Paul to be happy.
But I hate it here.

Ricky

Ellie

Joe

I miss my **friends.**

I miss my friends.
I miss SKATE CITY.
I went to SKATE CITY
all the time with my friends.

There's nowhere to skate here.
There's no skate park.

SKATE CITY

There's something else, too.
Paul has a son.
I will have a new stepbrother called Craig.
Craig is older than me. He's eighteen.

Craig – 12 years

Craig Snowboarding

I haven't met Craig yet.
He's been staying with his mum in America.
I will meet him tonight.

Messy!

Heavy metal music fan.

Videogame geek.

I don't think I want a stepbrother!

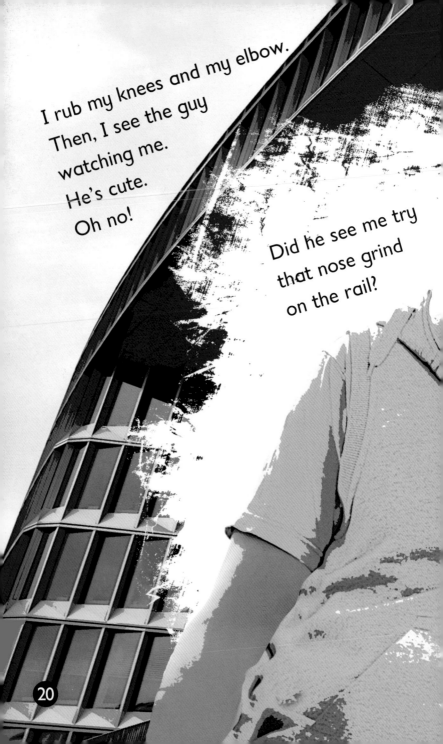

I rub my knees and my elbow.
Then, I see the guy
watching me.
He's cute.
Oh no!

Did he see me try
that nose grind
on the rail?

20

My life couldn't get any **worse.**

21

I stand up. I pick up my stuff.

My knees really hurt.

The cute guy is pulling my
deck from the tree.
He says, "You nearly did it."

I go bright red.
The guy saw me try that
nose grind on the rail.

23

"Try again," the guy says.
"Don't push down so hard
on the nose this time."

I look at the rail.
I think of the pain when
I hit the steps.
But I want to do it!
"OK," I say.

The guy hands
me my deck.

He says,

"Go for it."

I walk up the steps.
The rail looks so high.
I've never pulled a nose
grind like this before.

The guy smiles at me,

"You can do it!"

I push off.
I bend my knees.
I pull an ollie.

Yes!

I'm on the rail.

My front truck is
grinding down the rail.

Focus

Stay cool

I remember – *Don't push down so hard on the nose.*

The grind is fast and smooth!

33

The rail ends.
I fly through the air
and land just right.

I did it!

The guy says, "Wow! I could never grind that rail."

He says, "You are really good."

I like this guy. I say, "Thanks, I did what you said. It worked!"

I say, "You must be a skater?" He says, "Yes. I used to be."

We walk around
the town together.

He shows me some
great places to skate.

I like this guy.
I say, "I'm Sophie."
He smiles and says,
"I guessed."
I don't understand.
I say, "How did you guess?"

He says,
"I'm Craig."

GRIND - WHAT'S NEXT?

A GRAFFITI TAG
ON YOUR OWN

Write your name in large pencil letters on a piece of paper.

- Draw an outline around each letter. Look at the tags on pages 40–41 for ideas.

- Use chalk to colour the tag. Outline each letter in one colour and colour them in with another. Add highlights to your tag with white chalk.

- Spray hairspray over the tag to set it.

SKATER FILE
WITH A PARTNER

Find out more about skating using the internet and books.

- Look up different stunts.
  For example, ollie, grind and kickflip.

- Look up different obstacles. For example, halfpipe, handrail, steps.

  Make a SKATER FILE using your facts. Show what you have found out in words and pictures.

LET'S TALK
IN A GROUP

Imagine that Craig and Sophie decide to campaign for a skate park. The council ask them to present their case.

- Write down Sophie and Craig's arguments for a skate park.
- Write down the council's arguments against.
- Role-play the meeting. Did Sophie and Craig win their campaign?

SKATE PARK
ON YOUR OWN / WITH A PARTNER / IN A GROUP

Imagine you have been asked to design a skate park.

- Think of a name for the park.
- What obstacles will it have?

- What else does the park have? For example, a café, a shop, toilets, places to sit...
- Draw a plan of the skate park. Design a leaflet to advertise it.

45

IF YOU ENJOYED THIS BOOK, TRY THESE OTHER RIGHT NOW! BOOKS.

It's just an old, empty house.
Lauren must spend the night inside.
Just Lauren and the ghost...

Tonight, Vicky must make a choice. Stay in London with her boyfriend Chris. Or start a new life in Australia.

Dan sees the red car.
The keys are inside. Dan says to Andy, Sam and Jess, "Want to go for a drive?"

It's Saturday night.
Two angry guys. Two knives.
There's going to be a fight.

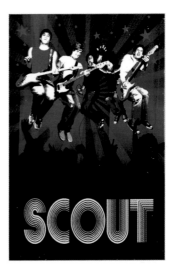

Tonight is the band's big
chance. Tonight, a record
company scout is at their gig!

Ed's platoon is under attack.
Another soldier is in danger.
Ed must risk his own life to
save him.

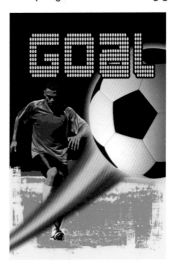

Today is Carl's trial with
City. There's just one place
up for grabs. But today,
everything is going wrong!